This Parent Wins

Set In Soul

© 2018 Tatiana Media LLC in partnership with Set In Soul LLC

978-1-7321075-0-2

Published by Tatiana Media LLC

For general information on our other products and services, please contact our Customer Support within the United States at support@setinsoul.com.

Tatiana Media LLC as well as Set In Soul LLC publishes its books in a variety of electronic formats. Some content that appears in print may not be available in electronic books.

This Journal Belongs To

Dedicated To The Parents That Continue To Move Forward. You Are A Blessing To Others. For This Reason Alone, You Are Blessed.

Table Of Contents

How To Use This Journal

To be a parent is an amazing lifetime job. To be a single parent is an amazing lifetime job that will require you to summon every last bit of energy within you to keep your household running. It is not an easy job but it is a fulfilling job that will require you to depend on God. Being a single parent doesn't make your family, your heart, and your efforts any less remarkable than anyone else's. With God, your child/ren are never motherless or fatherless.

There are times where feelings of discouragement, tiredness, anger, fear, resentment, loneliness and more show up as part of single parenthood. When you need a safe place to channel these feelings, this journal serves as that safe place. Regardless of whether you have help or you are doing this on your own, your feelings are valid. If you are interested in currently being the best single parent you can be, then you must first begin by taking care of you. This means nurturing yourself in a healthy and loving way. When you begin to ask yourself questions that will help you analyze your thoughts, actions, and patterns …. you will be able to release what needs to go in peace and learn to grow in love with yourself and the process. You are deserving of your best and so are your children. When you are truly in touch with who you are in this current season of your life and are truly honest about how you handle certain situations and how you could improve from it, you will begin to become the parent that wins. You win because your focus is on becoming better. You win because you give yourself the attention you deserve. You win because you realize that you are enough. That's how you win.

With this journal, it is recommended that you fill out each daily prompt page at night. This is the best time to reflect on your day and meditate. The freestyling sections are there for you to write down any extra thoughts you may have at any time. The motivational quotes sprinkled throughout this journal are there to encourage you and inspire you. This is your chance to release and talk to you about you and anything that deals with being a single parent. This journal is to be used when you are feeling happy, mad, excited, sad, discouraged, indifferent, and more. Filling out this journal over time will help you become the best single parent you can be regardless of what is going on. We know you are a winner and just want you to know this too. You are the parent that wins.

Time To Reflect

Time To Reflect

I Became A Parent At The Age Of:

I Became A Single Parent At The Age Of:

My Kid/s Names Is/Are:

I Became A Single Parent (Write The Date):

I Am A Single Parent Because:

Time To Reflect

When I Found Out I Was Going To Be A Single Parent, I:

As A Single Parent, I Am:

My Family Consists Of:

I Never Thought:

I Look Forward To:

Time To Reflect

As A Single Parent, I Am Responsible For:

As A Single Parent, I Experience:

My Current Income As A Single Parent:

As A Single Parent, I Know:

As A Single Parent, I Feel Guilty About:

Time To Reflect

Things I Would Have Done Differently:

What I Will Not Put Up With As A Single Parent:

I Have Been Angry For So Long About:

I Deal With My Anger/Disappointment By:

I Want To Get To A Place Where:

12

Time To Reflect

When It Comes To Money, I:

I Depend On:

When My Kid/s Need Something That Cost Money, I:

If I Need More Money, The Things I Can Do To Increase My Income:

My Current Income Makes Me Feel:

Time To Reflect

The Goals I Have For My Kid/s Are:

The Things I Plan To Start Doing With My Kid/s:

The Things I Can Do Or Have Tried To Do To Have A Better Relationship With My Child's/Children's Other Parent:

The Things My Child's/Children's Other Parent And I Agree On:

The Things I Believe I Need To Improve On As A Single Parent:

Time To Reflect

My Support System Consists Of:

What Motivates Me To Stay Strong As A Single Parent:

Is It Time To Start Dating?

The Response To The Question Above Is No Because I Feel Like The Best Time For Me To Start Dating Is (Only Answer If You Responded To The Prompt Above With The Answer Being No)?

Why Do I Really Want To Date?

Time To Reflect

Am I Currently Open To Dating?

Am I Currently Dating?

Is My Current Relationship Healthy For My Kid/s (Answer If Applicable)?

Values I Want In A Potential Stepparent:

My Kid/s Feel That My Current Partner Is (Answer If Applicable):

Time To Reflect

How Does My Child's/Children's Other Parent Feel About Who I Am Currently Dating (Answer If Applicable)?

How Do I Feel About My Child's/Children's Other Parent Dating (Answer If Applicable)?

How Do I Feel About My Child's/Children's Other Parent's Partner (Answer If Applicable)?

When I Feel Like Giving Up, I:

I Am Determined To:

Time To Reflect

I Want My Kid/s To Know:

What We Do As A Family Weekly:

I Am Okay With:

I Know I Can:

I Am Willing To:

Time To Reflect

I Am Grateful:

I've Thought Why Me About:

When I Drop Off My Kid/s At Their Other Parent's House, I Feel:

When I See The Other Parent, I Feel:

The Current Agreement We Have About The Kid/s:

Time To Reflect

Things My Kid/s Other Parent And I Disagree About When It Comes To
Raising Our Kid/s:

After Interacting With The Other Parent, I Feel:

I Am Disappointed About:

I Am Happy That:

My Kid/s Is/Are:

Time To Reflect

If It Wasn't For My Kid/s:

I Plan On:

I Feel Like Being A Single Parent Is:

The Next Time Around, I Know I Must:

Who Did I Disappoint Being A Single Parent?

Time To Reflect

I Hate That I Have To Tell My Kid/s:

Somehow, I Find A Way To:

My Life Has Changed For:

I Look At Being A Single Parent As:

What I Enjoy About Being A Single Parent:

Time To Reflect

When I Get Overwhelmed, I:

Seeing My Kid/s Remind Me That:

I Secretly:

What I Never Told Anyone:

Being Single For Some Time Has Changed:

Time To Reflect

I Want To Get Better At:

I Need Time For:

Playing Both Roles In My Household:

I Need Help With:

In The Future:

Time To Reflect

In The Future, I Want To Experience:

I Want To See My Kid/s:

I Still Believe:

I Will Not Give Up On:

I Want My Kid/s To Know The Truth About:

Time To Reflect

What Happened (Regarding Your Answer To The Previous Prompt)?

When Will I Tell Them (Regarding Your Answer To The Prompt Above)?

I Feel Like My Time With The Kid/s:

I Have Made The Decision To:

Positive Things I Am Working On For Myself:

Time To Reflect

My Kid/s Help Me To:

When The Kid/s Are Not With Me, I Feel:

When The Kid/s Are Not With Me, I Start To Think:

Being A Single Parent Has Affected My Kid/s By:

I Feel The Pressure To:

Time To Reflect

The Joys Of Being A Single Parent:

I Struggle With:

My Kid/s Empower Me:

When I Talk About Being A Single Parent, My Tone And Attitude Is Always:

Seeing Other Families With Both Parents Together, Makes Me Feel:

Time To Reflect

My Family Is Special Because:

I Love When:

I Am Great At:

I Discipline My Kid/s By:

I Teach My Kid/s That:

Time To Reflect

I Hope My Kid/s Will Learn:

Being A Single Parent Makes Me:

I Am At A Place In My Life Where:

I Know I Can't Control:

I Have Come To Terms With:

Time To Reflect

I Have Decided For Myself:

I Know I Deserve:

I Know I Am More Than:

I Am Working On Improving Within Myself:

Things I No Longer Take For Granted:

Time To Reflect

When It Comes To A Social Life, I Have To Work At It By:

My Current Daily Routine:

My Ideal Daily Routine:

As A Family, We Handle Adversity By:

I Am Always Positive About:

Time To Reflect

I Am Hopeful That:

I Find Myself:

I Am Raising My Kid/s To Be:

This Parent Wins Daily

This Parent Wins Daily

Date: Mood:

I Need: I've Let Go Of:

I've Made Time For Myself Today   I Smiled At:
By:

My Goals Today Were: What My Kid/s Said/Did That
                                               Made Me Laugh Today:

Tonight's Prayer For My Kids: Today I Spent Quality Time With
                                               My Kid/s By:

I Found Peace In: I Was A Proud Parent Today
                                               Because:

Tomorrow Will Be: _____.

This Parent Wins Daily

Date: Mood:

I Need: I've Let Go Of:

I've Made Time For Myself Today   I Smiled At:
By:

My Goals Today Were: What My Kid/s Said/Did That
                                         Made Me Laugh Today:

Tonight's Prayer For My Kids: Today I Spent Quality Time With
                                         My Kid/s By:

I Found Peace In: I Was A Proud Parent Today
                                         Because:

Tomorrow Will Be: _____.

This Parent Wins Daily

Date: Mood:

I Need: I've Let Go Of:

I've Made Time For Myself Today   I Smiled At:
By:

My Goals Today Were: What My Kid/s Said/Did That
                                        Made Me Laugh Today:

Tonight's Prayer For My Kids: Today I Spent Quality Time With
                                        My Kid/s By:

I Found Peace In: I Was A Proud Parent Today
                                        Because:

Tomorrow Will Be: _____.

My Mission Statement For My Family....

This Parent Wins Daily

Date: Mood:

I Need: I've Let Go Of:

I've Made Time For Myself Today   I Smiled At:
By:

My Goals Today Were: What My Kid/s Said/Did That
                                         Made Me Laugh Today:

Tonight's Prayer For My Kids: Today I Spent Quality Time With
                                         My Kid/s By:

I Found Peace In: I Was A Proud Parent Today
                                         Because:

Tomorrow Will Be: _____.

This Parent Wins Daily

Date: Mood:

I Need: I've Let Go Of:

I've Made Time For Myself Today   I Smiled At:
By:

My Goals Today Were: What My Kid/s Said/Did That
                                       Made Me Laugh Today:

Tonight's Prayer For My Kids: Today I Spent Quality Time With
                                       My Kid/s By:

I Found Peace In: I Was A Proud Parent Today
                                       Because:

Tomorrow Will Be: _____.

Trust Me. I Know What I Am Doing.
– God

This Parent Wins Daily

Date: Mood:

I Need: I've Let Go Of:

I've Made Time For Myself Today   I Smiled At:
By:

My Goals Today Were: What My Kid/s Said/Did That
                                               Made Me Laugh Today:

Tonight's Prayer For My Kids: Today I Spent Quality Time With
                                               My Kid/s By:

I Found Peace In: I Was A Proud Parent Today
                                               Because:

Tomorrow Will Be: _____.

This Parent Wins Daily

Date: Mood:

I Need: I've Let Go Of:

I've Made Time For Myself Today   I Smiled At:
By:

My Goals Today Were: What My Kid/s Said/Did That
                                         Made Me Laugh Today:

Tonight's Prayer For My Kids: Today I Spent Quality Time With
                                         My Kid/s By:

I Found Peace In: I Was A Proud Parent Today
                                         Because:

Tomorrow Will Be: _____.

Sometimes Walking Alone Makes You Stronger.

When
You Have
Extraordinary
Kids, You
Are Bound
To Have An
Extraordinary
Life.

This Parent Wins Daily

Date: Mood:

I Need: I've Let Go Of:

I've Made Time For Myself Today   I Smiled At:
By:

My Goals Today Were: What My Kid/s Said/Did That
                                         Made Me Laugh Today:

Tonight's Prayer For My Kids: Today I Spent Quality Time With
                                         My Kid/s By:

I Found Peace In: I Was A Proud Parent Today
                                         Because:

Tomorrow Will Be: _____.

This Parent Wins Daily

Date: Mood:

I Need: I've Let Go Of:

I've Made Time For Myself Today   I Smiled At:
By:

My Goals Today Were: What My Kid/s Said/Did That
                                         Made Me Laugh Today:

Tonight's Prayer For My Kids: Today I Spent Quality Time With
                                         My Kid/s By:

I Found Peace In: I Was A Proud Parent Today
                                         Because:

Tomorrow Will Be: _____.

A Letter To My Future Self....

This Parent Wins Daily

Date: Mood:

I Need: I've Let Go Of:

I've Made Time For Myself Today   I Smiled At:
By:

My Goals Today Were: What My Kid/s Said/Did That
                                         Made Me Laugh Today:

Tonight's Prayer For My Kids: Today I Spent Quality Time With
                                         My Kid/s By:

I Found Peace In: I Was A Proud Parent Today
                                         Because:

Tomorrow Will Be: _____.

This Parent Wins Daily

Date: Mood:

I Need: I've Let Go Of:

I've Made Time For Myself Today   I Smiled At:
By:

My Goals Today Were: What My Kid/s Said/Did That
                                         Made Me Laugh Today:

Tonight's Prayer For My Kids: Today I Spent Quality Time With
                                         My Kid/s By:

I Found Peace In: I Was A Proud Parent Today
                                         Because:

Tomorrow Will Be: _____.

My Personal Thoughts

This Parent Wins Daily

Date: Mood:

I Need: I've Let Go Of:

I've Made Time For Myself Today   I Smiled At:
By:

My Goals Today Were: What My Kid/s Said/Did That
                                          Made Me Laugh Today:

Tonight's Prayer For My Kids: Today I Spent Quality Time With
                                          My Kid/s By:

I Found Peace In: I Was A Proud Parent Today
                                          Because:

Tomorrow Will Be: _____.

This Parent Wins Daily

Date: Mood:

I Need: I've Let Go Of:

I've Made Time For Myself Today   I Smiled At:
By:

My Goals Today Were: What My Kid/s Said/Did That
                                    Made Me Laugh Today:

Tonight's Prayer For My Kids: Today I Spent Quality Time With
                                    My Kid/s By:

I Found Peace In: I Was A Proud Parent Today
                                    Because:

Tomorrow Will Be: _____.

A Letter To My Kid/s....

This Parent Wins Daily

Date: Mood:

I Need: I've Let Go Of:

I've Made Time For Myself Today   I Smiled At:
By:

My Goals Today Were: What My Kid/s Said/Did That
                                   Made Me Laugh Today:

Tonight's Prayer For My Kids: Today I Spent Quality Time With
                                   My Kid/s By:

I Found Peace In: I Was A Proud Parent Today
                                   Because:

Tomorrow Will Be: _____.

My Smile
Is Just
My First
Little
Love Note
To My
Kids.

So Busy
Loving My
Life That
I Have
No Time
For Hate,
Regret,
Or Fear.

This Parent Wins Daily

Date: Mood:

I Need: I've Let Go Of:

I've Made Time For Myself Today   I Smiled At:
By:

My Goals Today Were: What My Kid/s Said/Did That
                                   Made Me Laugh Today:

Tonight's Prayer For My Kids: Today I Spent Quality Time With
                                   My Kid/s By:

I Found Peace In: I Was A Proud Parent Today
                                   Because:

Tomorrow Will Be: _____.

This Parent Wins Daily

Date: Mood:

I Need: I've Let Go Of:

I've Made Time For Myself Today   I Smiled At:
By:

My Goals Today Were: What My Kid/s Said/Did That
                                         Made Me Laugh Today:

Tonight's Prayer For My Kids: Today I Spent Quality Time With
                                         My Kid/s By:

I Found Peace In: I Was A Proud Parent Today
                                         Because:

Tomorrow Will Be: _____.

This Parent Wins Daily

Date: Mood:

I Need: I've Let Go Of:

I've Made Time For Myself Today   I Smiled At:
By:

My Goals Today Were: What My Kid/s Said/Did That
                                           Made Me Laugh Today:

Tonight's Prayer For My Kids: Today I Spent Quality Time With
                                           My Kid/s By:

I Found Peace In: I Was A Proud Parent Today
                                           Because:

Tomorrow Will Be: _____.

What I Notice My Kid/s Like To Do....

My Personal Thoughts

This Parent Wins Daily

Date: Mood:

I Need: I've Let Go Of:

I've Made Time For Myself Today   I Smiled At:
By:

My Goals Today Were: What My Kid/s Said/Did That
                                         Made Me Laugh Today:

Tonight's Prayer For My Kids: Today I Spent Quality Time With
                                         My Kid/s By:

I Found Peace In: I Was A Proud Parent Today
                                         Because:

Tomorrow Will Be: _____.

This Parent Wins Daily

Date: Mood:

I Need: I've Let Go Of:

I've Made Time For Myself Today   I Smiled At:
By:

My Goals Today Were: What My Kid/s Said/Did That
                                         Made Me Laugh Today:

Tonight's Prayer For My Kids: Today I Spent Quality Time With
                                         My Kid/s By:

I Found Peace In: I Was A Proud Parent Today
                                         Because:

Tomorrow Will Be: _____.

One Bad Chapter Does Not Control The Outcome Of My Story.

This Parent Wins Daily

Date: Mood:

I Need: I've Let Go Of:

I've Made Time For Myself Today   I Smiled At:
By:

My Goals Today Were: What My Kid/s Said/Did That
                                        Made Me Laugh Today:

Tonight's Prayer For My Kids: Today I Spent Quality Time With
                                        My Kid/s By:

I Found Peace In: I Was A Proud Parent Today
                                        Because:

Tomorrow Will Be: _____.

This Parent Wins Daily

Date: Mood:

I Need: I've Let Go Of:

I've Made Time For Myself Today   I Smiled At:
By:

My Goals Today Were: What My Kid/s Said/Did That
                                         Made Me Laugh Today:

Tonight's Prayer For My Kids: Today I Spent Quality Time With
                                         My Kid/s By:

I Found Peace In: I Was A Proud Parent Today
                                         Because:

Tomorrow Will Be: _____.

My Personal Thoughts

Special Rituals The Kids
And I Share....

This Parent Wins Daily

Date: Mood:

I Need:

I've Let Go Of:

I've Made Time For Myself Today By:

I Smiled At:

My Goals Today Were:

What My Kid/s Said/Did That Made Me Laugh Today:

Tonight's Prayer For My Kids:

Today I Spent Quality Time With My Kid/s By:

I Found Peace In:

I Was A Proud Parent Today Because:

Tomorrow Will Be: _____.

This Parent Wins Daily

Date: Mood:

I Need: I've Let Go Of:

I've Made Time For Myself Today   I Smiled At:
By:

My Goals Today Were: What My Kid/s Said/Did That
                                         Made Me Laugh Today:

Tonight's Prayer For My Kids: Today I Spent Quality Time With
                                         My Kid/s By:

I Found Peace In: I Was A Proud Parent Today
                                         Because:

Tomorrow Will Be: _____.

I Operate From Love.

While
I May
Encounter
Some
Challenges,
I Still Feel
Blessed.

This Parent Wins Daily

Date: Mood:

I Need: I've Let Go Of:

I've Made Time For Myself Today   I Smiled At:
By:

My Goals Today Were: What My Kid/s Said/Did That
                                  Made Me Laugh Today:

Tonight's Prayer For My Kids: Today I Spent Quality Time With
                                  My Kid/s By:

I Found Peace In: I Was A Proud Parent Today
                                  Because:

Tomorrow Will Be: _____.

This Parent Wins Daily

Date: Mood:

I Need: I've Let Go Of:

I've Made Time For Myself Today   I Smiled At:
By:

My Goals Today Were: What My Kid/s Said/Did That
                                         Made Me Laugh Today:

Tonight's Prayer For My Kids: Today I Spent Quality Time With
                                         My Kid/s By:

I Found Peace In: I Was A Proud Parent Today
                                         Because:

Tomorrow Will Be: _____.

My Personal Thoughts

Traditions I Want To Establish....

This Parent Wins Daily

Date: Mood:

I Need: I've Let Go Of:

I've Made Time For Myself Today   I Smiled At:
By:

My Goals Today Were: What My Kid/s Said/Did That
                                         Made Me Laugh Today:

Tonight's Prayer For My Kids: Today I Spent Quality Time With
                                         My Kid/s By:

I Found Peace In: I Was A Proud Parent Today
                                         Because:

Tomorrow Will Be: _____.

This Parent Wins Daily

Date: Mood:

I Need: I've Let Go Of:

I've Made Time For Myself Today   I Smiled At:
By:

My Goals Today Were: What My Kid/s Said/Did That
                                               Made Me Laugh Today:

Tonight's Prayer For My Kids: Today I Spent Quality Time With
                                               My Kid/s By:

I Found Peace In: I Was A Proud Parent Today
                                               Because:

Tomorrow Will Be: _____.

This Parent Wins Daily

Date: Mood:

I Need: I've Let Go Of:

I've Made Time For Myself Today   I Smiled At:
By:

My Goals Today Were: What My Kid/s Said/Did That
                                         Made Me Laugh Today:

Tonight's Prayer For My Kids: Today I Spent Quality Time With
                                         My Kid/s By:

I Found Peace In: I Was A Proud Parent Today
                                         Because:

Tomorrow Will Be: _____.

I Choose To Be Present And Happy Than To Think About The Past And Wonder What If.

My Personal Thoughts

This Parent Wins Daily

Date: Mood:

I Need: I've Let Go Of:

I've Made Time For Myself Today   I Smiled At:
By:

My Goals Today Were: What My Kid/s Said/Did That
                                               Made Me Laugh Today:

Tonight's Prayer For My Kids: Today I Spent Quality Time With
                                               My Kid/s By:

I Found Peace In: I Was A Proud Parent Today
                                               Because:

Tomorrow Will Be: _____.

This Parent Wins Daily

Date: Mood:

I Need: I've Let Go Of:

I've Made Time For Myself Today   I Smiled At:
By:

My Goals Today Were: What My Kid/s Said/Did That
                                         Made Me Laugh Today:

Tonight's Prayer For My Kids: Today I Spent Quality Time With
                                         My Kid/s By:

I Found Peace In: I Was A Proud Parent Today
                                         Because:

Tomorrow Will Be: _____.

This Parent Wins Daily

Date: Mood:

I Need: I've Let Go Of:

I've Made Time For Myself Today   I Smiled At:
By:

My Goals Today Were: What My Kid/s Said/Did That
                                       Made Me Laugh Today:

Tonight's Prayer For My Kids: Today I Spent Quality Time With
                                       My Kid/s By:

I Found Peace In: I Was A Proud Parent Today
                                       Because:

Tomorrow Will Be: _____.

I Try My Best To Avoid Single Parent Burnout By....

I Am At A Place In Life Where I Am Accepting The Things I Cannot Change.

My Personal Thoughts

This Parent Wins Daily

Date: Mood:

I Need: I've Let Go Of:

I've Made Time For Myself Today   I Smiled At:
By:

My Goals Today Were: What My Kid/s Said/Did That
                                     Made Me Laugh Today:

Tonight's Prayer For My Kids: Today I Spent Quality Time With
                                     My Kid/s By:

I Found Peace In: I Was A Proud Parent Today
                                     Because:

Tomorrow Will Be: _____.

This Parent Wins Daily

Date: Mood:

I Need: I've Let Go Of:

I've Made Time For Myself Today   I Smiled At:
By:

My Goals Today Were: What My Kid/s Said/Did That
                                         Made Me Laugh Today:

Tonight's Prayer For My Kids: Today I Spent Quality Time With
                                         My Kid/s By:

I Found Peace In: I Was A Proud Parent Today
                                         Because:

Tomorrow Will Be: _____.

This Parent Wins Daily

Date: Mood:

I Need: I've Let Go Of:

I've Made Time For Myself Today   I Smiled At:
By:

My Goals Today Were: What My Kid/s Said/Did That
                                   Made Me Laugh Today:

Tonight's Prayer For My Kids: Today I Spent Quality Time With
                                   My Kid/s By:

I Found Peace In: I Was A Proud Parent Today
                                   Because:

Tomorrow Will Be: _____.

A Vision I Have For Myself And My Kid/s....

Some Days I Need Coffee, And Some Days My Coffee Needs Coffee.

This Parent Wins Daily

Date: Mood:

I Need: I've Let Go Of:

I've Made Time For Myself Today   I Smiled At:
By:

My Goals Today Were: What My Kid/s Said/Did That
                                         Made Me Laugh Today:

Tonight's Prayer For My Kids: Today I Spent Quality Time With
                                         My Kid/s By:

I Found Peace In: I Was A Proud Parent Today
                                         Because:

Tomorrow Will Be: _____.

This Parent Wins Daily

Date: Mood:

I Need: I've Let Go Of:

I've Made Time For Myself Today   I Smiled At:
By:

My Goals Today Were: What My Kid/s Said/Did That
                                   Made Me Laugh Today:

Tonight's Prayer For My Kids: Today I Spent Quality Time With
                                   My Kid/s By:

I Found Peace In: I Was A Proud Parent Today
                                   Because:

Tomorrow Will Be: _____.

This Parent Wins Daily

Date: Mood:

I Need: I've Let Go Of:

I've Made Time For Myself Today   I Smiled At:
By:

My Goals Today Were: What My Kid/s Said/Did That
                                         Made Me Laugh Today:

Tonight's Prayer For My Kids: Today I Spent Quality Time With
                                         My Kid/s By:

I Found Peace In: I Was A Proud Parent Today
                                         Because:

Tomorrow Will Be: _____.

My Personal Thoughts

This Parent Wins Daily

Date: Mood:

I Need: I've Let Go Of:

I've Made Time For Myself Today By: I Smiled At:

My Goals Today Were: What My Kid/s Said/Did That Made Me Laugh Today:

Tonight's Prayer For My Kids: Today I Spent Quality Time With My Kid/s By:

I Found Peace In: I Was A Proud Parent Today Because:

Tomorrow Will Be: _____.

This Parent Wins Daily

Date: Mood:

I Need: I've Let Go Of:

I've Made Time For Myself Today   I Smiled At:
By:

My Goals Today Were: What My Kid/s Said/Did That
                                         Made Me Laugh Today:

Tonight's Prayer For My Kids: Today I Spent Quality Time With
                                         My Kid/s By:

I Found Peace In: I Was A Proud Parent Today
                                         Because:

Tomorrow Will Be: _____.

This Parent Wins Daily

Date: Mood:

I Need: I've Let Go Of:

I've Made Time For Myself Today   I Smiled At:
By:

My Goals Today Were: What My Kid/s Said/Did That
                                   Made Me Laugh Today:

Tonight's Prayer For My Kids: Today I Spent Quality Time With
                                   My Kid/s By:

I Found Peace In: I Was A Proud Parent Today
                                   Because:

Tomorrow Will Be: _____.

I Have Let Go Of These False Beliefs About Myself And My Parenting Skills....

Everyday I Give The Love I Want To Receive.

My Child Is
The True
Definition Of
Unconditional
Love.

This Parent Wins Daily

Date: Mood:

I Need: I've Let Go Of:

I've Made Time For Myself Today   I Smiled At:
By:

My Goals Today Were: What My Kid/s Said/Did That
                                   Made Me Laugh Today:

Tonight's Prayer For My Kids: Today I Spent Quality Time With
                                   My Kid/s By:

I Found Peace In: I Was A Proud Parent Today
                                   Because:

Tomorrow Will Be: _____.

This Parent Wins Daily

Date: Mood:

I Need: I've Let Go Of:

I've Made Time For Myself Today   I Smiled At:
By:

My Goals Today Were: What My Kid/s Said/Did That
                                         Made Me Laugh Today:

Tonight's Prayer For My Kids: Today I Spent Quality Time With
                                         My Kid/s By:

I Found Peace In: I Was A Proud Parent Today
                                         Because:

Tomorrow Will Be: _____.

This Parent Wins Daily

Date: Mood:

I Need: I've Let Go Of:

I've Made Time For Myself Today   I Smiled At:
By:

My Goals Today Were: What My Kid/s Said/Did That
                                         Made Me Laugh Today:

Tonight's Prayer For My Kids: Today I Spent Quality Time With
                                         My Kid/s By:

I Found Peace In: I Was A Proud Parent Today
                                         Because:

Tomorrow Will Be: _____.

My Personal Thoughts

Parenting With Love Is The Most Important Job That God Will Give You.

This Parent Wins Daily

Date: Mood:

I Need: I've Let Go Of:

I've Made Time For Myself Today   I Smiled At:
By:

My Goals Today Were: What My Kid/s Said/Did That
                                         Made Me Laugh Today:

Tonight's Prayer For My Kids: Today I Spent Quality Time With
                                         My Kid/s By:

I Found Peace In: I Was A Proud Parent Today
                                         Because:

Tomorrow Will Be: _____.

Things I Have Stopped Complaining About....

My Personal Thoughts

This Parent Wins Daily

Date: Mood:

I Need: I've Let Go Of:

I've Made Time For Myself Today   I Smiled At:
By:

My Goals Today Were: What My Kid/s Said/Did That
                                         Made Me Laugh Today:

Tonight's Prayer For My Kids: Today I Spent Quality Time With
                                         My Kid/s By:

I Found Peace In: I Was A Proud Parent Today
                                         Because:

Tomorrow Will Be: _____.

This Parent Wins Daily

Date: Mood:

I Need: I've Let Go Of:

I've Made Time For Myself Today   I Smiled At:
By:

My Goals Today Were: What My Kid/s Said/Did That
                                         Made Me Laugh Today:

Tonight's Prayer For My Kids: Today I Spent Quality Time With
                                         My Kid/s By:

I Found Peace In: I Was A Proud Parent Today
                                         Because:

Tomorrow Will Be: _____.

This Parent Wins Daily

Date: Mood:

I Need: I've Let Go Of:

I've Made Time For Myself Today   I Smiled At:
By:

My Goals Today Were: What My Kid/s Said/Did That
                                          Made Me Laugh Today:

Tonight's Prayer For My Kids: Today I Spent Quality Time With
                                          My Kid/s By:

I Found Peace In: I Was A Proud Parent Today
                                          Because:

Tomorrow Will Be: _____.

I Will Always Believe In My Child.

More Hugs. Less Shouts.

This Parent Wins Daily

Date: Mood:

I Need: I've Let Go Of:

I've Made Time For Myself Today   I Smiled At:
By:

My Goals Today Were: What My Kid/s Said/Did That
                                 Made Me Laugh Today:

Tonight's Prayer For My Kids: Today I Spent Quality Time With
                                 My Kid/s By:

I Found Peace In: I Was A Proud Parent Today
                                 Because:

Tomorrow Will Be: _____.

This Parent Wins Daily

Date: Mood:

I Need: I've Let Go Of:

I've Made Time For Myself Today   I Smiled At:
By:

My Goals Today Were: What My Kid/s Said/Did That
                                         Made Me Laugh Today:

Tonight's Prayer For My Kids: Today I Spent Quality Time With
                                         My Kid/s By:

I Found Peace In: I Was A Proud Parent Today
                                         Because:

Tomorrow Will Be: _____.

This Parent Wins Daily

Date: Mood:

I Need: I've Let Go Of:

I've Made Time For Myself Today   I Smiled At:
By:

My Goals Today Were: What My Kid/s Said/Did That
                                         Made Me Laugh Today:

Tonight's Prayer For My Kids: Today I Spent Quality Time With
                                         My Kid/s By:

I Found Peace In: I Was A Proud Parent Today
                                         Because:

Tomorrow Will Be: _____.

I Will Be The Best Example Of What I Want My Kids To Become And Still Hope That They Strive To Become Better Than Me.

My Personal Thoughts

I Believe A Good Child And Parent Relationship Is....

This Parent Wins Daily

Date: Mood:

I Need: I've Let Go Of:

I've Made Time For Myself Today   I Smiled At:
By:

My Goals Today Were: What My Kid/s Said/Did That
                                         Made Me Laugh Today:

Tonight's Prayer For My Kids: Today I Spent Quality Time With
                                         My Kid/s By:

I Found Peace In: I Was A Proud Parent Today
                                         Because:

Tomorrow Will Be: _____.

This Parent Wins Daily

Date: Mood:

I Need: I've Let Go Of:

I've Made Time For Myself Today   I Smiled At:
By:

My Goals Today Were: What My Kid/s Said/Did That
                                               Made Me Laugh Today:

Tonight's Prayer For My Kids: Today I Spent Quality Time With
                                               My Kid/s By:

I Found Peace In: I Was A Proud Parent Today
                                               Because:

Tomorrow Will Be: _____.

I Know I Can. End Of Story.

This Parent Wins Daily

Date: Mood:

I Need: I've Let Go Of:

I've Made Time For Myself Today   I Smiled At:
By:

My Goals Today Were: What My Kid/s Said/Did That
                                         Made Me Laugh Today:

Tonight's Prayer For My Kids: Today I Spent Quality Time With
                                         My Kid/s By:

I Found Peace In: I Was A Proud Parent Today
                                         Because:

Tomorrow Will Be: _____.

My Personal Thoughts

This Parent Wins Daily

Date: Mood:

I Need: I've Let Go Of:

I've Made Time For Myself Today   I Smiled At:
By:

My Goals Today Were: What My Kid/s Said/Did That
                                   Made Me Laugh Today:

Tonight's Prayer For My Kids: Today I Spent Quality Time With
                                   My Kid/s By:

I Found Peace In: I Was A Proud Parent Today
                                   Because:

Tomorrow Will Be: _____.

This Parent Wins Daily

Date: Mood:

I Need: I've Let Go Of:

I've Made Time For Myself Today   I Smiled At:
By:

My Goals Today Were: What My Kid/s Said/Did That
                                       Made Me Laugh Today:

Tonight's Prayer For My Kids: Today I Spent Quality Time With
                                       My Kid/s By:

I Found Peace In: I Was A Proud Parent Today
                                       Because:

Tomorrow Will Be: _____.

Things That Use To Bother Me That No Longer Do....

No One
Can Bring
Me Down
When I
Have A Kid
That Brings
Me Up.

This Parent Wins Daily

Date: Mood:

I Need: I've Let Go Of:

I've Made Time For Myself Today   I Smiled At:
By:

My Goals Today Were: What My Kid/s Said/Did That
                                         Made Me Laugh Today:

Tonight's Prayer For My Kids: Today I Spent Quality Time With
                                         My Kid/s By:

I Found Peace In: I Was A Proud Parent Today
                                         Because:

Tomorrow Will Be: _____.

This Parent Wins Daily

Date: Mood:

I Need: I've Let Go Of:

I've Made Time For Myself Today   I Smiled At:
By:

My Goals Today Were: What My Kid/s Said/Did That
                                             Made Me Laugh Today:

Tonight's Prayer For My Kids: Today I Spent Quality Time With
                                             My Kid/s By:

I Found Peace In: I Was A Proud Parent Today
                                             Because:

Tomorrow Will Be: _____.

This Parent Wins Daily

Date: Mood:

I Need: I've Let Go Of:

I've Made Time For Myself Today   I Smiled At:
By:

My Goals Today Were: What My Kid/s Said/Did That
                                               Made Me Laugh Today:

Tonight's Prayer For My Kids: Today I Spent Quality Time With
                                               My Kid/s By:

I Found Peace In: I Was A Proud Parent Today
                                               Because:

Tomorrow Will Be: _____.

I Am Too
Busy Being
The Best
Parent I
Can Be, To
Spend Time
Proving It
To Others.

My Kid Is The Real Hero.

I Give God My Weakness In Exchange For His Strength.

Current Household
Rules Are....

This Parent Wins Daily

Date: Mood:

I Need: I've Let Go Of:

I've Made Time For Myself Today   I Smiled At:
By:

My Goals Today Were: What My Kid/s Said/Did That
                                         Made Me Laugh Today:

Tonight's Prayer For My Kids: Today I Spent Quality Time With
                                         My Kid/s By:

I Found Peace In: I Was A Proud Parent Today
                                         Because:

Tomorrow Will Be: _____.

This Parent Wins Daily

Date: Mood:

I Need: I've Let Go Of:

I've Made Time For Myself Today   I Smiled At:
By:

My Goals Today Were: What My Kid/s Said/Did That
                               Made Me Laugh Today:

Tonight's Prayer For My Kids: Today I Spent Quality Time With
                               My Kid/s By:

I Found Peace In: I Was A Proud Parent Today
                               Because:

Tomorrow Will Be: _____.

My Grace Is Sufficient For You, For My Strength Is Made Perfect In Weakness.

2 Corinthians 12:9

No One Will Take Away My Inner Peace.

This Parent Wins Daily

Date: Mood:

I Need: I've Let Go Of:

I've Made Time For Myself Today   I Smiled At:
By:

My Goals Today Were: What My Kid/s Said/Did That
                               Made Me Laugh Today:

Tonight's Prayer For My Kids: Today I Spent Quality Time With
                                My Kid/s By:

I Found Peace In: I Was A Proud Parent Today
                                Because:

Tomorrow Will Be: _____.

This Parent Wins Daily

Date: Mood:

I Need: I've Let Go Of:

I've Made Time For Myself Today   I Smiled At:
By:

My Goals Today Were: What My Kid/s Said/Did That
                                         Made Me Laugh Today:

Tonight's Prayer For My Kids: Today I Spent Quality Time With
                                         My Kid/s By:

I Found Peace In: I Was A Proud Parent Today
                                         Because:

Tomorrow Will Be: _____.

My Personal Thoughts

This Parent Wins Daily

Date: Mood:

I Need: I've Let Go Of:

I've Made Time For Myself Today   I Smiled At:
By:

My Goals Today Were: What My Kid/s Said/Did That
                               Made Me Laugh Today:

Tonight's Prayer For My Kids: Today I Spent Quality Time With
                               My Kid/s By:

I Found Peace In: I Was A Proud Parent Today
                               Because:

Tomorrow Will Be: _____.

This Parent Wins Daily

Date: Mood:

I Need: I've Let Go Of:

I've Made Time For Myself Today   I Smiled At:
By:

My Goals Today Were: What My Kid/s Said/Did That
                                               Made Me Laugh Today:

Tonight's Prayer For My Kids: Today I Spent Quality Time With
                                               My Kid/s By:

I Found Peace In: I Was A Proud Parent Today
                                               Because:

Tomorrow Will Be: _____.

This Parent Wins Daily

Date: Mood:

I Need: I've Let Go Of:

I've Made Time For Myself Today   I Smiled At:
By:

My Goals Today Were: What My Kid/s Said/Did That
                                         Made Me Laugh Today:

Tonight's Prayer For My Kids: Today I Spent Quality Time With
                                         My Kid/s By:

I Found Peace In: I Was A Proud Parent Today
                                         Because:

Tomorrow Will Be: _____.

I Like To Lose Myself In....

This Parent Wins Daily

Date: Mood:

I Need: I've Let Go Of:

I've Made Time For Myself Today   I Smiled At:
By:

My Goals Today Were: What My Kid/s Said/Did That
                                                      Made Me Laugh Today:

Tonight's Prayer For My Kids: Today I Spent Quality Time With
                                                      My Kid/s By:

I Found Peace In: I Was A Proud Parent Today
                                                      Because:

Tomorrow Will Be: _____.

Being A Single Parent Is Tough, But So Am I.

Each Day Is A New Day To Get Better And Better At Giving Love.

This Parent Wins Daily

Date: Mood:

I Need: I've Let Go Of:

I've Made Time For Myself Today   I Smiled At:
By:

My Goals Today Were: What My Kid/s Said/Did That
                                        Made Me Laugh Today:

Tonight's Prayer For My Kids: Today I Spent Quality Time With
                                        My Kid/s By:

I Found Peace In: I Was A Proud Parent Today
                                        Because:

Tomorrow Will Be: _____.

This Parent Wins Daily

Date: Mood:

I Need: I've Let Go Of:

I've Made Time For Myself Today   I Smiled At:
By:

My Goals Today Were: What My Kid/s Said/Did That
                                         Made Me Laugh Today:

Tonight's Prayer For My Kids: Today I Spent Quality Time With
                                         My Kid/s By:

I Found Peace In: I Was A Proud Parent Today
                                         Because:

Tomorrow Will Be: _____.

This Parent Wins Daily

Date: Mood:

I Need: I've Let Go Of:

I've Made Time For Myself Today   I Smiled At:
By:

My Goals Today Were: What My Kid/s Said/Did That
                                        Made Me Laugh Today:

Tonight's Prayer For My Kids: Today I Spent Quality Time With
                                        My Kid/s By:

I Found Peace In: I Was A Proud Parent Today
                                        Because:

Tomorrow Will Be: _____.

My Personal Thoughts

I
Appreciate
Bedtime.

This Parent Wins Daily

Date: Mood:

I Need: I've Let Go Of:

I've Made Time For Myself Today   I Smiled At:
By:

My Goals Today Were: What My Kid/s Said/Did That
                                         Made Me Laugh Today:

Tonight's Prayer For My Kids: Today I Spent Quality Time With
                                         My Kid/s By:

I Found Peace In: I Was A Proud Parent Today
                                         Because:

Tomorrow Will Be: _____.

10 Songs That Motivate Me

1.

2.

3.

4.

5.

6.

7.

8.

9.

10.

I Know My Child Is Always Watching, So I Lead By Being And Not Just By Saying.

My Personal Thoughts

This Parent Wins Daily

Date: Mood:

I Need: I've Let Go Of:

I've Made Time For Myself Today   I Smiled At:
By:

My Goals Today Were: What My Kid/s Said/Did That
                                   Made Me Laugh Today:

Tonight's Prayer For My Kids: Today I Spent Quality Time With
                                   My Kid/s By:

I Found Peace In: I Was A Proud Parent Today
                                   Because:

Tomorrow Will Be: _____.

This Parent Wins Daily

Date: Mood:

I Need:

I've Let Go Of:

I've Made Time For Myself Today By:

I Smiled At:

My Goals Today Were:

What My Kid/s Said/Did That Made Me Laugh Today:

Tonight's Prayer For My Kids:

Today I Spent Quality Time With My Kid/s By:

I Found Peace In:

I Was A Proud Parent Today Because:

Tomorrow Will Be: _____.

My Destiny Isn't Determined By My Relationship Status.

This Parent Wins Daily

Date: Mood:

I Need: I've Let Go Of:

I've Made Time For Myself Today   I Smiled At:
By:

My Goals Today Were: What My Kid/s Said/Did That
                                         Made Me Laugh Today:

Tonight's Prayer For My Kids: Today I Spent Quality Time With
                                         My Kid/s By:

I Found Peace In: I Was A Proud Parent Today
                                         Because:

Tomorrow Will Be: _____.

This Parent Wins Daily

Date: Mood:

I Need: I've Let Go Of:

I've Made Time For Myself Today   I Smiled At:
By:

My Goals Today Were: What My Kid/s Said/Did That
                               Made Me Laugh Today:

Tonight's Prayer For My Kids: Today I Spent Quality Time With
                               My Kid/s By:

I Found Peace In: I Was A Proud Parent Today
                               Because:

Tomorrow Will Be: _____.

Five Prayers That Keep Me Grounded....

1.

2.

3.

4.

5.

This Parent Wins Daily

Date: Mood:

I Need: I've Let Go Of:

I've Made Time For Myself Today   I Smiled At:
By:

My Goals Today Were: What My Kid/s Said/Did That
                                         Made Me Laugh Today:

Tonight's Prayer For My Kids: Today I Spent Quality Time With
                                         My Kid/s By:

I Found Peace In: I Was A Proud Parent Today
                                         Because:

Tomorrow Will Be: _____.

This Parent Wins Daily

Date: Mood:

I Need: I've Let Go Of:

I've Made Time For Myself Today   I Smiled At:
By:

My Goals Today Were: What My Kid/s Said/Did That
                                   Made Me Laugh Today:

Tonight's Prayer For My Kids: Today I Spent Quality Time With
                                   My Kid/s By:

I Found Peace In: I Was A Proud Parent Today
                                   Because:

Tomorrow Will Be: _____.

My Personal Thoughts

This Parent Wins Daily

Date: Mood:

I Need: I've Let Go Of:

I've Made Time For Myself Today   I Smiled At:
By:

My Goals Today Were: What My Kid/s Said/Did That
                                         Made Me Laugh Today:

Tonight's Prayer For My Kids: Today I Spent Quality Time With
                                         My Kid/s By:

I Found Peace In: I Was A Proud Parent Today
                                         Because:

Tomorrow Will Be: _____.

This Parent Wins Daily

Date: Mood:

I Need: I've Let Go Of:

I've Made Time For Myself Today   I Smiled At:
By:

My Goals Today Were: What My Kid/s Said/Did That
                                         Made Me Laugh Today:

Tonight's Prayer For My Kids: Today I Spent Quality Time With
                                         My Kid/s By:

I Found Peace In: I Was A Proud Parent Today
                                         Because:

Tomorrow Will Be: _____.

You Can Be A Single Parent, And Still Go After Your Dreams.

This Parent Wins Daily

Date: Mood:

I Need: I've Let Go Of:

I've Made Time For Myself Today   I Smiled At:
By:

My Goals Today Were: What My Kid/s Said/Did That
                                         Made Me Laugh Today:

Tonight's Prayer For My Kids: Today I Spent Quality Time With
                                         My Kid/s By:

I Found Peace In: I Was A Proud Parent Today
                                         Because:

Tomorrow Will Be: _____.

174

My Kid/s Make Me Proud By....

God Is A Father To The Fatherless And A Mother To The Motherless.

This Parent Wins Daily

Date: Mood:

I Need: I've Let Go Of:

I've Made Time For Myself Today   I Smiled At:
By:

My Goals Today Were: What My Kid/s Said/Did That
                                   Made Me Laugh Today:

Tonight's Prayer For My Kids: Today I Spent Quality Time With
                                   My Kid/s By:

I Found Peace In: I Was A Proud Parent Today
                                   Because:

Tomorrow Will Be: _____.

This Parent Wins Daily

Date: Mood:

I Need: I've Let Go Of:

I've Made Time For Myself Today   I Smiled At:
By:

My Goals Today Were: What My Kid/s Said/Did That
                                         Made Me Laugh Today:

Tonight's Prayer For My Kids: Today I Spent Quality Time With
                                         My Kid/s By:

I Found Peace In: I Was A Proud Parent Today
                                         Because:

Tomorrow Will Be: _____.

This Parent Wins Daily

Date: Mood:

I Need: I've Let Go Of:

I've Made Time For Myself Today   I Smiled At:
By:

My Goals Today Were: What My Kid/s Said/Did That
                                         Made Me Laugh Today:

Tonight's Prayer For My Kids: Today I Spent Quality Time With
                                         My Kid/s By:

I Found Peace In: I Was A Proud Parent Today
                                         Because:

Tomorrow Will Be: _____.

This Parent Wins Daily

Date: Mood:

I Need: I've Let Go Of:

I've Made Time For Myself Today   I Smiled At:
By:

My Goals Today Were: What My Kid/s Said/Did That
                                   Made Me Laugh Today:

Tonight's Prayer For My Kids: Today I Spent Quality Time With
                                   My Kid/s By:

I Found Peace In: I Was A Proud Parent Today
                                   Because:

Tomorrow Will Be: _____.

I'm Raising My Child To Know God.

Being A Single Parent Doesn't Come With Instructions And Yet I'm Still Doing A Great Job.

This Parent Wins Daily

Date: Mood:

I Need: I've Let Go Of:

I've Made Time For Myself Today   I Smiled At:
By:

My Goals Today Were: What My Kid/s Said/Did That
                                          Made Me Laugh Today:

Tonight's Prayer For My Kids: Today I Spent Quality Time With
                                          My Kid/s By:

I Found Peace In: I Was A Proud Parent Today
                                          Because:

Tomorrow Will Be: _____.

This Parent Wins Daily

Date: Mood:

I Need: I've Let Go Of:

I've Made Time For Myself Today   I Smiled At:
By:

My Goals Today Were: What My Kid/s Said/Did That
                                       Made Me Laugh Today:

Tonight's Prayer For My Kids: Today I Spent Quality Time With
                                       My Kid/s By:

I Found Peace In: I Was A Proud Parent Today
                                       Because:

Tomorrow Will Be: _____.

This Parent Wins Daily

Date: Mood:

I Need: I've Let Go Of:

I've Made Time For Myself Today   I Smiled At:
By:

My Goals Today Were: What My Kid/s Said/Did That
                                                Made Me Laugh Today:

Tonight's Prayer For My Kids: Today I Spent Quality Time With
                                                My Kid/s By:

I Found Peace In: I Was A Proud Parent Today
                                                Because:

Tomorrow Will Be: _____.

A List Of Personal Hobbies That I Now Do With My Kid/s....

My Personal Thoughts

This Parent Wins Daily

Date: Mood:

I Need: I've Let Go Of:

I've Made Time For Myself Today   I Smiled At:
By:

My Goals Today Were: What My Kid/s Said/Did That
                                         Made Me Laugh Today:

Tonight's Prayer For My Kids: Today I Spent Quality Time With
                                         My Kid/s By:

I Found Peace In: I Was A Proud Parent Today
                                         Because:

Tomorrow Will Be: _____.

This Parent Wins Daily

Date: Mood:

I Need: I've Let Go Of:

I've Made Time For Myself Today   I Smiled At:
By:

My Goals Today Were: What My Kid/s Said/Did That
                                   Made Me Laugh Today:

Tonight's Prayer For My Kids: Today I Spent Quality Time With
                                   My Kid/s By:

I Found Peace In: I Was A Proud Parent Today
                                   Because:

Tomorrow Will Be: _____.

Being A Single Parent Is About Discovering The Strengths You Didn't Know You Had.

This Parent Wins Daily

Date: Mood:

I Need: I've Let Go Of:

I've Made Time For Myself Today   I Smiled At:
By:

My Goals Today Were: What My Kid/s Said/Did That
                               Made Me Laugh Today:

Tonight's Prayer For My Kids: Today I Spent Quality Time With
                               My Kid/s By:

I Found Peace In: I Was A Proud Parent Today
                               Because:

Tomorrow Will Be: _____.

This Parent Wins Daily

Date: Mood:

I Need: I've Let Go Of:

I've Made Time For Myself Today   I Smiled At:
By:

My Goals Today Were: What My Kid/s Said/Did That
                                  Made Me Laugh Today:

Tonight's Prayer For My Kids: Today I Spent Quality Time With
                                  My Kid/s By:

I Found Peace In: I Was A Proud Parent Today
                                  Because:

Tomorrow Will Be: _____.

This Parent Wins Daily

Date: Mood:

I Need: I've Let Go Of:

I've Made Time For Myself Today   I Smiled At:
By:

My Goals Today Were: What My Kid/s Said/Did That
                                               Made Me Laugh Today:

Tonight's Prayer For My Kids: Today I Spent Quality Time With
                                               My Kid/s By:

I Found Peace In: I Was A Proud Parent Today
                                               Because:

Tomorrow Will Be: _____.

My Personal Thoughts

I Will Exhale The Negative And Inhale The Positive.

This Parent Wins Daily

Date: Mood:

I Need: I've Let Go Of:

I've Made Time For Myself Today   I Smiled At:
By:

My Goals Today Were: What My Kid/s Said/Did That
                                         Made Me Laugh Today:

Tonight's Prayer For My Kids: Today I Spent Quality Time With
                                         My Kid/s By:

I Found Peace In: I Was A Proud Parent Today
                                         Because:

Tomorrow Will Be: _____.

This Parent Wins Daily

Date: Mood:

I Need: I've Let Go Of:

I've Made Time For Myself Today   I Smiled At:
By:

My Goals Today Were: What My Kid/s Said/Did That
                                         Made Me Laugh Today:

Tonight's Prayer For My Kids: Today I Spent Quality Time With
                                         My Kid/s By:

I Found Peace In: I Was A Proud Parent Today
                                         Because:

Tomorrow Will Be: _____.

This Parent Wins Daily

Date: Mood:

I Need: I've Let Go Of:

I've Made Time For Myself Today   I Smiled At:
By:

My Goals Today Were: What My Kid/s Said/Did That
                                         Made Me Laugh Today:

Tonight's Prayer For My Kids: Today I Spent Quality Time With
                                         My Kid/s By:

I Found Peace In: I Was A Proud Parent Today
                                         Because:

Tomorrow Will Be: _____.

Books I Will Read For Self Improvement....

By His Grace, My Children Are Blessed.

This Parent Wins Daily

Date: Mood:

I Need: I've Let Go Of:

I've Made Time For Myself Today   I Smiled At:
By:

My Goals Today Were: What My Kid/s Said/Did That
                                          Made Me Laugh Today:

Tonight's Prayer For My Kids: Today I Spent Quality Time With
                                          My Kid/s By:

I Found Peace In: I Was A Proud Parent Today
                                          Because:

Tomorrow Will Be: _____.

This Parent Wins Daily

Date: Mood:

I Need: I've Let Go Of:

I've Made Time For Myself Today   I Smiled At:
By:

My Goals Today Were: What My Kid/s Said/Did That
                                   Made Me Laugh Today:

Tonight's Prayer For My Kids: Today I Spent Quality Time With
                                   My Kid/s By:

I Found Peace In: I Was A Proud Parent Today
                                   Because:

Tomorrow Will Be: _____.

My Personal Thoughts

This Parent Wins Daily

Date: Mood:

I Need: I've Let Go Of:

I've Made Time For Myself Today   I Smiled At:
By:

My Goals Today Were: What My Kid/s Said/Did That
                                           Made Me Laugh Today:

Tonight's Prayer For My Kids: Today I Spent Quality Time With
                                           My Kid/s By:

I Found Peace In: I Was A Proud Parent Today
                                           Because:

Tomorrow Will Be: _____.

This Parent Wins Daily

Date: Mood:

I Need: I've Let Go Of:

I've Made Time For Myself Today   I Smiled At:
By:

My Goals Today Were: What My Kid/s Said/Did That
                                         Made Me Laugh Today:

Tonight's Prayer For My Kids: Today I Spent Quality Time With
                                         My Kid/s By:

I Found Peace In: I Was A Proud Parent Today
                                         Because:

Tomorrow Will Be: _____.

This Parent Wins Daily

Date: Mood:

I Need: I've Let Go Of:

I've Made Time For Myself Today   I Smiled At:
By:

My Goals Today Were: What My Kid/s Said/Did That
                                         Made Me Laugh Today:

Tonight's Prayer For My Kids: Today I Spent Quality Time With
                                         My Kid/s By:

I Found Peace In: I Was A Proud Parent Today
                                         Because:

Tomorrow Will Be: _____.

206

Things And People I'd Like To Say No To....

This Parent Wins Daily

Date: Mood:

I Need: I've Let Go Of:

I've Made Time For Myself Today   I Smiled At:
By:

My Goals Today Were: What My Kid/s Said/Did That
                                               Made Me Laugh Today:

Tonight's Prayer For My Kids: Today I Spent Quality Time With
                                               My Kid/s By:

I Found Peace In: I Was A Proud Parent Today
                                               Because:

Tomorrow Will Be: _____.

My Kid's Opinion Of Whether I'm A Good Parent Or Not Is All That Matters.

This Parent Wins Daily

Date: Mood:

I Need: I've Let Go Of:

I've Made Time For Myself Today   I Smiled At:
By:

My Goals Today Were: What My Kid/s Said/Did That
                                               Made Me Laugh Today:

Tonight's Prayer For My Kids: Today I Spent Quality Time With
                                               My Kid/s By:

I Found Peace In: I Was A Proud Parent Today
                                               Because:

Tomorrow Will Be: _____.

This Parent Wins Daily

Date: Mood:

I Need: I've Let Go Of:

I've Made Time For Myself Today   I Smiled At:
By:

My Goals Today Were: What My Kid/s Said/Did That
                                         Made Me Laugh Today:

Tonight's Prayer For My Kids: Today I Spent Quality Time With
                                         My Kid/s By:

I Found Peace In: I Was A Proud Parent Today
                                         Because:

Tomorrow Will Be: _____.

This Parent Wins Daily

Date: Mood:

I Need: I've Let Go Of:

I've Made Time For Myself Today   I Smiled At:
By:

My Goals Today Were: What My Kid/s Said/Did That
                                         Made Me Laugh Today:

Tonight's Prayer For My Kids: Today I Spent Quality Time With
                                         My Kid/s By:

I Found Peace In: I Was A Proud Parent Today
                                         Because:

Tomorrow Will Be: _____.

I'm Becoming The Person I Should've Been A Long Time Ago. Happy And Free.

I Love That Everyday I Am Improving.

My Personal Thoughts

This Parent Wins Daily

Date: Mood:

I Need: I've Let Go Of:

I've Made Time For Myself Today   I Smiled At:
By:

My Goals Today Were: What My Kid/s Said/Did That
                                   Made Me Laugh Today:

Tonight's Prayer For My Kids: Today I Spent Quality Time With
                                   My Kid/s By:

I Found Peace In: I Was A Proud Parent Today
                                   Because:

Tomorrow Will Be: _____.

This Parent Wins Daily

Date: Mood:

I Need: I've Let Go Of:

I've Made Time For Myself Today   I Smiled At:
By:

My Goals Today Were: What My Kid/s Said/Did That
                                                     Made Me Laugh Today:

Tonight's Prayer For My Kids: Today I Spent Quality Time With
                                                     My Kid/s By:

I Found Peace In: I Was A Proud Parent Today
                                                     Because:

Tomorrow Will Be: _____.

This Parent Wins Daily

Date: Mood:

I Need: I've Let Go Of:

I've Made Time For Myself Today   I Smiled At:
By:

My Goals Today Were: What My Kid/s Said/Did That
                                             Made Me Laugh Today:

Tonight's Prayer For My Kids: Today I Spent Quality Time With
                                             My Kid/s By:

I Found Peace In: I Was A Proud Parent Today
                                             Because:

Tomorrow Will Be: _____.

This Parent Wins Daily

Date: Mood:

I Need: I've Let Go Of:

I've Made Time For Myself Today   I Smiled At:
By:

My Goals Today Were: What My Kid/s Said/Did That
                                         Made Me Laugh Today:

Tonight's Prayer For My Kids: Today I Spent Quality Time With
                                         My Kid/s By:

I Found Peace In: I Was A Proud Parent Today
                                         Because:

Tomorrow Will Be: _____.

I Like To Mediate On....

My Personal Thoughts

This Parent Wins Daily

Date: Mood:

I Need: I've Let Go Of:

I've Made Time For Myself Today   I Smiled At:
By:

My Goals Today Were: What My Kid/s Said/Did That
                                           Made Me Laugh Today:

Tonight's Prayer For My Kids: Today I Spent Quality Time With
                                           My Kid/s By:

I Found Peace In: I Was A Proud Parent Today
                                           Because:

Tomorrow Will Be: _____.

222

This Parent Wins Daily

Date: Mood:

I Need: I've Let Go Of:

I've Made Time For Myself Today   I Smiled At:
By:

My Goals Today Were: What My Kid/s Said/Did That
                                   Made Me Laugh Today:

Tonight's Prayer For My Kids: Today I Spent Quality Time With
                                   My Kid/s By:

I Found Peace In: I Was A Proud Parent Today
                                   Because:

Tomorrow Will Be: _____.

This Parent Wins Daily

Date: Mood:

I Need: I've Let Go Of:

I've Made Time For Myself Today   I Smiled At:
By:

My Goals Today Were: What My Kid/s Said/Did That
                                         Made Me Laugh Today:

Tonight's Prayer For My Kids: Today I Spent Quality Time With
                                         My Kid/s By:

I Found Peace In: I Was A Proud Parent Today
                                         Because:

Tomorrow Will Be: _____.

Love, Respect And Support.

I Show Love By Spending Time.

This Parent Wins Daily

Date: Mood:

I Need: I've Let Go Of:

I've Made Time For Myself Today   I Smiled At:
By:

My Goals Today Were: What My Kid/s Said/Did That
                               Made Me Laugh Today:

Tonight's Prayer For My Kids: Today I Spent Quality Time With
                               My Kid/s By:

I Found Peace In: I Was A Proud Parent Today
                               Because:

Tomorrow Will Be: _____.

My Personal Thoughts

This Parent Wins Daily

Date: Mood:

I Need: I've Let Go Of:

I've Made Time For Myself Today   I Smiled At:
By:

My Goals Today Were: What My Kid/s Said/Did That
                                          Made Me Laugh Today:

Tonight's Prayer For My Kids: Today I Spent Quality Time With
                                          My Kid/s By:

I Found Peace In: I Was A Proud Parent Today
                                          Because:

Tomorrow Will Be: _____.

Family Always Comes First.

I've Got This.

My Motivational Story....

This Parent Wins Daily

Date: Mood:

I Need: I've Let Go Of:

I've Made Time For Myself Today   I Smiled At:
By:

My Goals Today Were: What My Kid/s Said/Did That
                                               Made Me Laugh Today:

Tonight's Prayer For My Kids: Today I Spent Quality Time With
                                               My Kid/s By:

I Found Peace In: I Was A Proud Parent Today
                                               Because:

Tomorrow Will Be: _____.

This Parent Wins Daily

Date: Mood:

I Need: I've Let Go Of:

I've Made Time For Myself Today   I Smiled At:
By:

My Goals Today Were: What My Kid/s Said/Did That
                                         Made Me Laugh Today:

Tonight's Prayer For My Kids: Today I Spent Quality Time With
                                         My Kid/s By:

I Found Peace In: I Was A Proud Parent Today
                                         Because:

Tomorrow Will Be: _____.

This Parent Wins Daily

Date: Mood:

I Need: I've Let Go Of:

I've Made Time For Myself Today   I Smiled At:
By:

My Goals Today Were: What My Kid/s Said/Did That
                                          Made Me Laugh Today:

Tonight's Prayer For My Kids: Today I Spent Quality Time With
                                          My Kid/s By:

I Found Peace In: I Was A Proud Parent Today
                                          Because:

Tomorrow Will Be: _____.

This Parent Wins Daily

Date: Mood:

I Need: I've Let Go Of:

I've Made Time For Myself Today   I Smiled At:
By:

My Goals Today Were: What My Kid/s Said/Did That
                                         Made Me Laugh Today:

Tonight's Prayer For My Kids: Today I Spent Quality Time With
                                         My Kid/s By:

I Found Peace In: I Was A Proud Parent Today
                                         Because:

Tomorrow Will Be: _____.

I Choose To Stay Positive Because I Am Grateful For What I've Got.

I Have Become Better Because Of My Kids.

This Parent Wins Daily

Date: Mood:

I Need: I've Let Go Of:

I've Made Time For Myself Today   I Smiled At:
By:

My Goals Today Were: What My Kid/s Said/Did That
                                        Made Me Laugh Today:

Tonight's Prayer For My Kids: Today I Spent Quality Time With
                                        My Kid/s By:

I Found Peace In: I Was A Proud Parent Today
                                        Because:

Tomorrow Will Be: _____.

My Personal Thoughts

My Child Comes First.

This Parent Wins Daily

Date: Mood:

I Need: I've Let Go Of:

I've Made Time For Myself Today   I Smiled At:
By:

My Goals Today Were: What My Kid/s Said/Did That
                                         Made Me Laugh Today:

Tonight's Prayer For My Kids: Today I Spent Quality Time With
                                         My Kid/s By:

I Found Peace In: I Was A Proud Parent Today
                                         Because:

Tomorrow Will Be: _____.

Once I Promised Myself Better, I Said I Would Never Look Back.

Made in the USA
Monee, IL
27 April 2020